Bee -&- Me

A STORY ABOUT FRIENDSHIP
BY
ALISON JAY

Old Barn Books

BEE AWARE!

When bees fly from flower to flower, they help plants to grow all over the world.
Without bees, it's hard to grow food or flowers. As cities get bigger,
there are fewer flowers in the world. And fewer bees.

You can help, by planting flowers. The good news is, bees love the most colourful and
best-smelling flowers. They don't have to be expensive plants – bees love weeds too.
Good bee flowers:

Dandelion	Lavender	Sunflower
Heather	Red or White Clover	Sweetpea
Honeysuckle	Rose	Tulip

Bees love herbs, such as Mint, Rosemary, Sage and Thyme – you can plant these in pots on your windowsill.

Bees also need dry, dark, hiding places, to make their nests. They like to crawl inside little pipes,
into log piles or under an upturned flowerpot. If you have a garden, leave a little
corner undisturbed to encourage bugs and bees.

Don't try to touch or pick up the bees, though – they just might sting you!

For my Mum, Maureen, a bee's best friend.
– AJ

AN OLD BARN BOOK

First published in the UK in 2016 by Old Barn Books Ltd
www.oldbarnbooks.com

Distributed in the UK by Bounce Sales & Marketing and
in Australia and New Zealand by Walker Books Ltd.

The illustrations were created using alkyd oil paints.

Design by Nghiem Ta
Pre-press and Production by Hinotori Media

FIRST EDITION

ISBN 978-1-91064-605-2

10 9 8 7 6 5 4 3 2 1

Printed in Malaysia

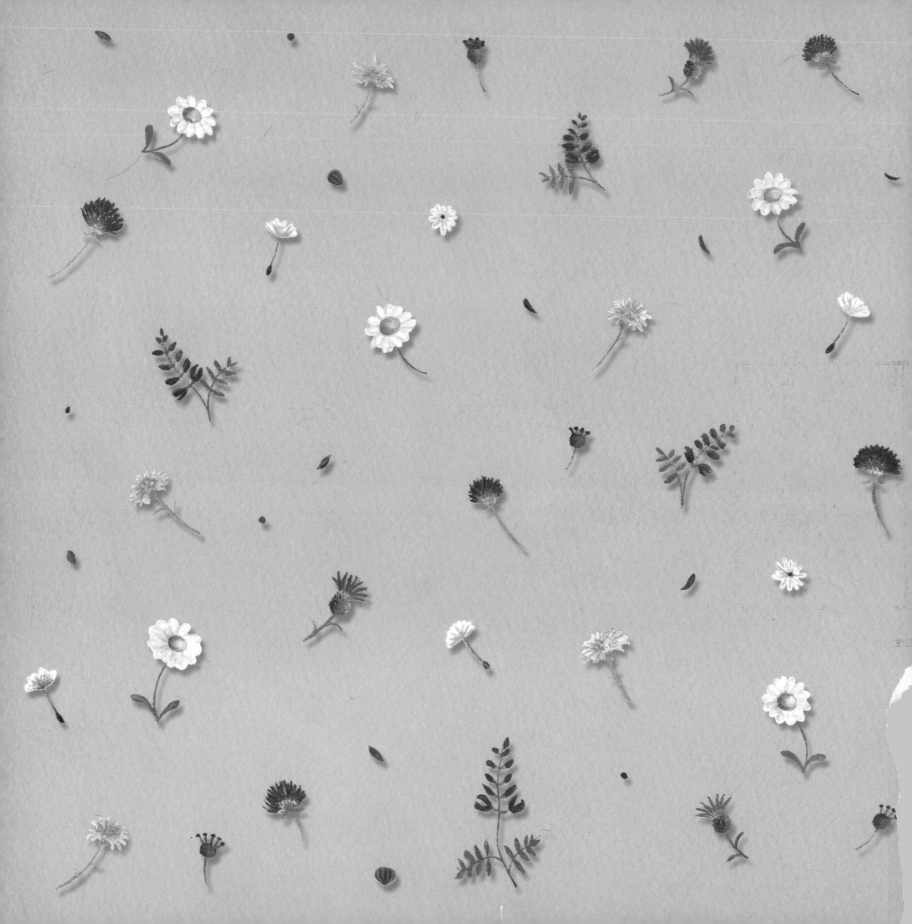